GCSE WJEC English
The Workbook
Reading Non-Fiction and Media Texts

This book is for anyone doing **GCSE WJEC English** at higher level.

It contains lots of **tricky questions** designed to hone your **reading skills** — because that's the only way you'll get any **better**.

It's also got some daft bits in to try and make the whole experience at least vaguely entertaining for you.

<u>What CGP is all about</u>

Our sole aim here at CGP is to produce the highest quality books — carefully written, immaculately presented and dangerously close to being funny.

Then we work our socks off to get them out to you — at the cheapest possible prices.

CONTENTS

Section One — Purpose and Audience

The Audience 1
The Purpose of the Text... 2
Texts that Persuade or Argue 3
Texts that Inform, Entertain or Advise 4
Formal Style and Informal Style 5
Personal Tone and Impersonal Tone 6

Section Two — Following an Argument

Following an Argument 7
Evaluating an Argument... 8
Facts and Opinions.. 9
Generalisations and Counter-arguments 10
Rhetoric and Bias 11

Section Three — Presentation and Layout

Headlines and Subheadings 12
Graphics and Captions 13
Text Boxes and Text Columns 14
Bullet Points and Numbered Lists 15
Font Styles and Formatting.. 16
Presentation and Layout — Overview 17

Section Four — Writing Techniques

Descriptive Language 18
Metaphors, Similes and Analogies 19
Personification, Alliteration and Onomatopoeia 20
Irony and Sarcasm 21
Technical and Emotive Language 22
Structure 23
Writing Techniques — Overview 24

Section Five — Exam Techniques

Search and Find Questions 25
P.E.E. 26
Writing in Paragraphs 27
Reading with Insight 28
Comparing Texts 29

Section Six — Sample Exam

Sample Exam — Questions 30
Sample Exam — Text 31
Sample Exam — Text 32
Sample Exam — Text 33
Mark Scheme — Question A1 34
Sample Answers — Question A1 35
Mark Scheme — Question A2 36
Sample Answers — Question A2 37
Mark Scheme — Question A3 38
Sample Answers — Question A3 39
Mark Scheme — Question A4 40
Sample Answers — Question A4 41

Section Seven — Practice Exam

Practice Exam — Questions 42
Practice Exam — Text 43
Practice Exam — Text 44

Published by Coordination Group Publications Ltd.

Editors:
Tim Burne
Katherine Craig
Charley Darbishire
Thomas Harte
Katherine Reed
Edward Robinson
Laurence Stamford
Jennifer Underwood

Contributors:
John Bowyer
Roland Haynes

Acknowledgements:
The publisher would like to thank the following copyright holders for permission to reproduce texts and images.

www.direct.gov.uk
'Voluntary work abroad', www.direct.gov.uk © Crown Copyright

Médecins Sans Frontières
'Eyewitness' article © 2005 Médecins Sans Frontières

Kadir van Lohuizen / Noor
'Eyewitness' photograph © Kadir van Lohuizen / Noor

NI Syndication
'Climate change brings Eiger to earth' by Steven Swinford © NI Syndication

The Random House Group Ltd.
Extract from 'The Beckoning Silence' by Joe Simpson published by Jonathan Cape.
Reprinted by permission of The Random House Group Ltd.

The Travel Library / Rex Features
Photograph 'Ski hut in front of Eiger mountain' © The Travel Library / Rex Features

Every effort has been made to locate copyright holders and obtain permission to reproduce texts and images. For those texts and images where it has been difficult to trace the originator of the work, we would be grateful for information. If any copyright holder would like us to make an amendment to the acknowledgements, please notify us and we will gladly update the book at the next reprint. Thank you.

ISBN: 978 1 84762 109 2

With thanks to Jennifer Underwood, Nicola Woodfin and Julia Murphy for the proofreading.
With thanks to Laura Phillips for the copyright research.

Groovy website: www.cgpbooks.co.uk

Jolly bits of clipart from CorelDRAW®

Printed by Elanders Hindson Ltd, Newcastle upon Tyne.

The Audience

Q1 For each sentence, circle the word which best describes the audience it is aimed at. The first one has been done for you.

a) "Do you yearn for a simpler, more reliable way of managing your finances?"

children /(adults)

b) "When buying a used car, try to get as much information from the dealer as you can."

experts / novices

c) "The financial opportunities presented by China's expanding economy are becoming more and more attractive."

tourists / business people

Q2 For each of the extracts below, write down the type of audience you think it is intended for, and briefly explain how you know.

a) "This position requires a flexible approach and a 'can-do' attitude."

....

....

b) "Before applying for a course, do plenty of research on the institution and its reputation."

....

....

Q3 What sort of people would you expect to read these publications?

a) *The Rough Guide to Turkey* ....

b) *The Times Educational Supplement* ....

c) *The Big Book of Car Games* ....

Q4 Read the text below and answer the question underneath. [MINI-ESSAY QUESTION]

Are you looking for a cool summer job?

We've got loads of temporary vacancies with no experience required!

All you need is some free time, a positive attitude and plenty of energy. If you've got your own wheels that's even better!

Picking... packing... stacking... waiting... waitressing... and TONS of others!

With Spondon Summer Jobs you can:
• gain great work experience
• make a few quid
• make new friends

Whatever you fancy, we can sort you out with a job that suits you down to the ground.
Interested? Call Jackie on 0547 262 626.

How does the advert aim to appeal directly to younger readers? Look at:
• the language used
• the content of the advertisement
• the font styles and presentation used

You'll need to use a separate sheet of paper to answer the mini-essay questions.

The Purpose of the Text

Q1   Draw lines to match each type of text to its main purpose.

a)   "Who could disagree with the fact that children should eat healthily?"

b)   "As the train moved south, first crawling, then increasing to a steady gallop, the scenery gradually changed from the flat and drab to the dramatic and beautiful."

c)   "Shop around for the best quote — some insurers are much more expensive than others."

d)   "Tomorrow, there will be scattered showers in the north-west."

to entertain

to inform

to persuade

to advise

Q2   Put each of the following types of text in the correct place in the table, based on its main purpose. The first one has been done for you. You may find that some of these fit into more than one column.

a charity advertisement	an article about the Industrial Revolution
a cake recipe	a film review
a newspaper editorial	an agony aunt column in a magazine
a leaflet from a political party	an instruction manual for a computer
a cartoon in a newspaper	a leaflet with tips on how to give up smoking

Texts that inform	Texts that entertain	Texts that argue or persuade	Texts that advise
		a charity advertisement	

Q3   Read the extract below, which was taken from a leaflet about a local election, then answer the question about it.

It is high time the people of this parish took a stand. We must tell the council: "enough is enough — *no more tax increases*." Time after time we have been told that this is the final time it will happen; and then what do we find? Another council tax increase. We are told that "vital improvements" will be made to local roads and services — yet time and again they fail to deliver.

Are we really expected to believe things will be any different this time? We must send out a clear message that we will not be taken for fools again. By voting for Sandy Green in the forthcoming council elections you can put an end to the growing amount of money leaving your pocket for no good reason.

What persuasive techniques does the writer of this text use to try to achieve her purpose?

MINI-ESSAY QUESTION

Texts that Persuade or Argue

Q1 Write an **A** for "argue a point" or a **P** for "persuade you to do something" to show the purpose of each of the following sentences.

a) "The barbaric practice of bear-baiting must be stopped completely and immediately."

b) "If you really want to make a difference, fill in this form and set up a monthly donation to help support our hard-working volunteers."

c) "By joining our march and signing this petition, you will be helping to put an end to this disgraceful act of cruelty."

d) "The decision to switch off the country's analogue TV signal is nothing more than a cynical attempt to boost sales of electrical equipment."

Q2 Read the extract below. Write down whether you think its purpose is to argue or to persuade, then briefly explain your answer.

> The bad language used by youngsters today is disgraceful. What's more, they seem to have no respect for authority, and society is a worse place as a result.

Purpose ....

Explanation ....

....

....

Q3 Read the extract from a leaflet below and then answer the question about it underneath.

Come to Oxton Aquarium — you'll have a whale of a time!

Oxton Aquarium is the only place in the county where you can see local and exotic species of fish and sea mammals all in one place.

Experience the magic of the deep as you are surrounded by the underwater world. You could be eyed up by an octopus, shaken by a shark or peered at by pike!

Whatever your age, you're guaranteed a fantastic time.

Entry costs: Adult — £6 Child — £3 Family ticket — £15

Oxton Aquarium — a great family day out!

Before you dive in to answering this question, make sure you're clear about what the writer's purpose is.

How does the presentation and choice of language help the leaflet to achieve its purpose?

MINI-ESSAY QUESTION

Texts that Inform, Entertain or Advise

Q1   Read the text below, then circle the word that best describes its purpose.

> A stern telling-off after bad behaviour is often all that is needed to ensure your child grows into a responsible, considerate individual.

advise   entertain

Q2   From the text below, pick out two words or phrases which are advisory and another two which are entertaining.

> Thai food can be startlingly hot, so watch out! The chefs round here get through chillies like you wouldn't believe — though some relief comes from the creamy coconut milk that tames the fire of the burning hot curries. For the adventurous, the colourful cuisine of the north-east makes liberal use of lime juice, garlic and fermented fish, contributing to its distinctive pungency.

a)   Meant to advise: 1) .... 2) ....

b)   Meant to entertain: 1) .... 2) ....

Q3   Read the two texts below, then say which text is informative and which text is entertaining. Write a brief explanation for each answer.

a)

> The Battle of Hastings was fought on October 14th, 1066 in a field near Hastings in East Sussex. It was during this encounter that the invading Normans, led by William the Conqueror, achieved their most important victory over the Anglo-Saxons, led by King Harold II.

This text is **entertaining / informative** because ....

....

....

b)

> The battle was furious and bloody, with vast numbers of soldiers being brutally slain. At one stage the English were fooled into thinking that they had won the battle. They stormed towards their enemy, only to find themselves ambushed and mercilessly torn to shreds.

This text is **entertaining / informative** because ....

....

....

Formal Style and Informal Style

Q1   For each pair of sentences, underline the more formal sentence.

> Sorry Sir, we don't accept credit cards — you're going to have to go in the kitchen and wash up.

a)   "Sorry! We don't take credit cards."
      "Customers are advised that we do not accept credit cards."

b)   "It is essential to ensure that you have the correct tools before proceeding."
      "Check you've got the proper kit to hand before you go any further."

c)   "Worried about rising debts? We've got all the info you need to sort your finances out."
      "If you have financial complications, contact our advisors at the following address."

Q2   Put each language feature in the correct column, based on where you would usually expect to find it.

non-standard English

standard English

complex sentences

simple sentences

chatty tone

serious tone

contractions (e.g. "don't")

impersonal style

personal style

humour

Formal texts	Informal texts

Q3   The text below is taken from a travel journal. Is the style of the text formal or informal?
      Write down three pieces of evidence from the text that back up your answer.

> At this point I was starting to get a tad — how shall I put it? — narked off. It's one thing being patient, accepting the fact that things don't always go to plan and that now and then delays just happen. It's quite another to be told, after paying good money for a ticket on the grounds that it's taking you to Town A, that apparently for no good reason we're taking a little detour through Village B, River C and Swamp D.
>
> I was finding it more and more difficult to follow what I had figured was the local way of dealing with difficulties — smiling and pretending to find the grim industrial scenery interesting.

The style is .... because:

1) ....

2) ....

3) ....

I like your style...

The style a writer chooses has to be appropriate for the intended audience. Keep this in mind in the exam — it'll make your answer a lot more relevant than if you just describe what the style is.

6

Personal Tone and Impersonal Tone

Q1 Write a **P** for "personal" or an **I** for "impersonal" to describe the tone that would usually be created by each technique.

a) written in first person ☐

b) written in passive voice ☐

c) openly biased ☐

d) neutral tone ☐

e) lots of facts used ☐

f) sounds emotional ☐

g) slang used ☐

h) formal language used ☐

Q2 Decide whether the text below has a personal or an impersonal tone. Find three pieces of evidence from the text to support your answer.

> There is a growing feeling that the situation concerning air pollution needs to be addressed. The number of individuals suffering from breathing problems in the city has been steadily increasing for years, with levels of particulate matter and nitrogen oxides soaring to new heights. Possible solutions are to be discussed at the next city council meeting.

The tone is **personal / impersonal** because:

1) ....

2) ....

3) ....

Q3 Use the following extract from an agony aunt column to answer the questions at the bottom of the page.

> Dear Rowena
>
> You poor thing, you're really down in the dumps, aren't you? I know it's hard to believe but your life will improve — you just need to take control over things again. Concentrate on what you used to be like, when you were more confident and enjoying life.
>
> One thing that's definitely worth a shot is consulting a career guidance counsellor. If you haven't got time for this then there are plenty of books on choosing the right job that I can recommend.
>
> The main thing to remember is that you're the boss of your own life — so take charge!

a) What techniques does the writer use to create a friendly, personal style in her writing? **MINI-ESSAY QUESTION**

b) How does this personal tone make the writing well suited to the target audience? **MINI-ESSAY QUESTION**

Section One — Purpose and Audience

Following an Argument

Q1   The text below is a letter printed by the *Daily Duncaster* local newspaper.
Read it and then answer the questions which follow.

> Dear Sir,
>
> I was horrified to read your article about the new soft drink "Swampy Water" being served in the tuck shop at Duncaster Primary School. This dangerous fad for drinking green, gungy water is clearly idiotic. Firstly, young children might get confused and think it's all right to drink *real* swamp water. I know from my time in the Territorial Army that this can make you very ill indeed. Secondly, "Swampy Water" is full of unhealthy sugar and additives — how else would it be that lurid green colour? Last but not least, the drink is expensive and means children don't have money left over to buy normal, healthy snacks. To conclude, "Swampy Water" should be removed from the tuck shop at Duncaster Primary School immediately.
>
> Yours faithfully,
> Gerry Bowness

a)   What is the **main** argument of the letter? Tick the correct option below.

☐ Drinking swamp water can make you ill.

☐ "Swampy Water" is unhealthy because it contains additives and sugar.

☐ "Swampy Water" shouldn't be on sale in Duncaster Primary School.

b)   Write down three points the writer makes to support his argument.
Write them using your own words.

1. ....

2. ....

3. ....

Q2   Read the following text then answer the question which follows.

> I love the colour pink. I love birds. I really love flamingos. How could anyone dislike them? They're the most fascinating, mysterious and beautiful birds in the world! That's why I'm starting a campaign to persuade people to sponsor flamingos in zoos. By donating a few pounds, people can help fund the setting up of breeding programmes for rare flamingo species. The head keeper at my local zoo, Jane Sutton, says, "Flamingos really are wonderful animals. Any donations would be much appreciated."

The table below shows the techniques used by the writer in their argument.
Fill in the table by picking out examples of each technique.

Technique	Example from text
repetition of words / phrases	
rhetorical question	
expert opinion	
exaggeration	

Evaluating an Argument

Q1   Which of the following would be **bad** to use in an argument? Tick the correct answers.

☐ inconsistencies   ☐ irony

☐ formal tone   ☐ factual inaccuracies

☐ out-of-date examples   ☐ points backed up with examples

☐ confusing explanations   ☐ persuasive language techniques

Q2   Read the following text. Describe one good point and one bad
point about the way the author has written her argument.

> The greatest television presenter of all time is Terry Wogan. When he first appeared on television
> in 1865, Wogan astonished everyone with his energy, enthusiasm and sparkling wit. He had a star
> quality which all previous television presenters lacked. Who could fail to be charmed by him?

A **good** point about this argument is ....

....

....

A **bad** point about this argument is ....

....

....

Q3   The notice below argues that a Neighbourhood Group is necessary, to persuade people to join up.
Read it and answer the question underneath.

Volunteers Needed for Salem Street Neighbourhood Group

No one wants to find litter and dog dirt on the pavement outside their front door. No one wants to have
graffiti scratched on their car. No one wants to be woken up in the middle of the night by loud music or
people arguing in the street. But, sadly, these things happen all the time in Salem Street. We all deserve
to live in a **pleasant, safe, clean** street. And if we join together **we can make it happen**.

- A committee of Salem Street residents is being formed to look at issues like anti-social behaviour, litter and noise
  levels. It's an opportunity for **us**, the people who live in Salem Street, to be proactive and **improve our community**.

- Similar street committees in the Runford area have proved **very effective** in reducing anti-social behaviour, e.g.
  Midden Avenue, which used to suffer from high levels of litter and graffiti, is now a very clean, pleasant street.

- Helping with the committee won't take up much of your time — but it will make a **big difference** to Salem Street.
  Come along and find out more about the committee at our first meeting in **Rixy's Bingo Hall, 8pm, 16th May**.

How effectively does this notice persuade? Write about:

MINI-ESSAY
QUESTION

- examples the writer uses to persuade the reader
- language devices the writer uses
- whether the leaflet achieves its purpose

Not bad, shame about the ranting...

When evaluating an argument, try and think of good and bad points about it. It's important to
back up your points with examples though. Just saying, "this argument is rubbish" won't do.

Facts and Opinions

Q1 Write down whether the following statements are opinions, facts or false facts.

a) London is the capital city of the UK. ....

b) Glasgow would be a better capital city of Scotland than Edinburgh. ....

c) Manchester is the capital city of England. ....

Q2 Read the statements below. For each one, say whether you think it is a fact or an opinion and explain your choice.

It's not always clear if something is a fact or an opinion — you have to work it out for yourself.

a) "Water boils at 100 degrees Celsius."

....

....

b) "As Madonna gets older, her music gets better."

....

....

Q3 Read the text below. It was taken from a newspaper article.
After you've read it, answer the questions below.

We're All Getting Older

Edward Lightburn

From The Daily Splurge, Thursday 2nd March 2006

We're all living longer and longer. In 1900 in the USA, people could expect to reach 47 years. That was the average life expectancy. In 2000 it was 77 years and the trend is continuing. It might not be long until most people live 'til they're in their nineties, or even over one hundred.

What are we all going to be doing when we're eighty-something? At the moment, old people don't really get a good deal. As soon as they're too troublesome for their families, they get booted out of home and shipped off to the nearest "care home". And at these places, they'll be patronised, prodded and poked like sick animals: "Does Sarah want her din-dins now? It's her favourite..." It's not something to look forward to, is it?

It used to be that the elderly were respected for their wisdom. Now they're treated like the waste product of society, thrown out and left to rot in their care homes; the landfill sites of modern British humanity.

a) Write down two facts and two opinions from the text.

Well, I wanted to do something special for your 130th...

Facts:

1. ....

2. ....

Opinions:

1. ....

2. ....

b) What do you think the author's attitude to old people is?
Use evidence from the text to back up your answer.

MINI-ESSAY QUESTION

Generalisations and Counter-arguments

Q1   Tick the statements which are generalisations.

a)   Gardening programmes on TV are all aimed at older viewers. ☐

b)   There are different types of rose you can grow in your garden. ☐

c)   My Aunt Daphne has a crush on Alan Titchmarsh. ☐

d)   Alan Titchmarsh is adored by women everywhere. ☐

Aunt Daphne was the notorious 'Gardener's World' streaker.

Q2   What is a counter-argument?

....

....

Q3   Read the following article and then answer the questions which follow.

> Film critics usually dismiss 40s movie heart-throb Robert Mitchum as a dumb hunk of an actor. They claim his sleepy-eyed, laidback performances were lazy and lacklustre. They argue that he never took risks with his acting and assume that he lacked the technical acting ability of other 40s stars like Spencer Tracy and Laurence Olivier.
>
> But how can anybody who has seen his terrifying performance as a murderous preacher in 'The Night of the Hunter' claim that Mitchum never took risks? How can anybody who has seen his touching, vulnerable performance in 'Ryan's Daughter' claim he had no technical acting ability?
>
> The work of many other 1940s movie stars now looks out-of-date and hammy. But Mitchum's films have aged well — the naturalism and humour of his acting are truly immortal.

a)   Which of the following quotes from the article sums up the writer's attitude to Robert Mitchum? Tick the correct one.

☐   "his sleepy-eyed, laidback performances were lazy and lacklustre"

☐   "the naturalism and humour of his acting are truly immortal"

b)   Write down three generalisations which the writer makes in this article.

1. ....

2. ....

3. ....

c)   How effective is the writer's use of generalisation and counter-argument in this article?   MINI-ESSAY QUESTION

Counter Arguments — like Tiddly-Winks in a fight...

Generalisations and counter-arguments are sneaky persuasive techniques that writers use.
You need to be able to spot when a writer has used them **and** discuss how effective they are.

Rhetoric and Bias

Q1   Draw lines to match up each persuasive technique to the sentence which uses it.

   a)   **rhetorical question**   i)   Nothing is more disgusting than a mouldy sandwich.

   b)   **repetition of words/phrases** ii) Who on earth would want to eat a mouldy sandwich?

   c)   **exaggeration**   iii) I hate mould. I hate sandwiches. I really hate mouldy sandwiches.

Q2   Are the following texts biased or unbiased? Explain your answers.

   a)   By far the best hobby for young people is the card game "cribbage". All young people from the ages of eight to eighteen adore playing cribbage. It's easy to learn, doesn't need much equipment and provides hours of fun.

   I think the text is **biased / unbiased** because ....

   ....

   ....

   ....

   b)   In Orkney, you can visit the remains of a Neolithic (Stone Age) village called Skara Brae. The village was inhabited about 5000 years ago. You can see the remains of walls, doorways, fireplaces and stone "furniture".

   I think the text is **biased / unbiased** because ....

   ....

   ....

   ....

Q3   Read the following extract from a travel brochure and answer the question which follows.

> ## Malliwest Resort Hotels
>
> Everyone daydreams. When you're stuck in the office — dealing with tricky customers, struggling with spreadsheets, drinking tepid tea — can you honestly say you haven't dreamt of lying on a sublime beach in a luxury resort, sipping cocktails and being waited on hand and foot?
>
> At Malliwest Resorts you can make your dreams a reality. Only at Malliwest Resorts can you reserve a private beach so that no one else can see what you look like in your swimming costume. Only at Malliwest Resorts can you order your favourite meal and have it made specially. Only at Malliwest Resorts can you ring room service at 4am and get a polite response!
>
> Malliwest Resorts' top priority is to make sure you have the **holiday of a lifetime**. If you book before 20th June, you'll get 15% off the price of your holiday. Surely this is an offer to fulfil anyone's dreams?

How does the writer use rhetorical language to persuade the reader?   MINI-ESSAY QUESTION

Headlines and Subheadings

Q1 Draw lines to connect each term with the descriptions below.
The descriptions may apply to both terms.

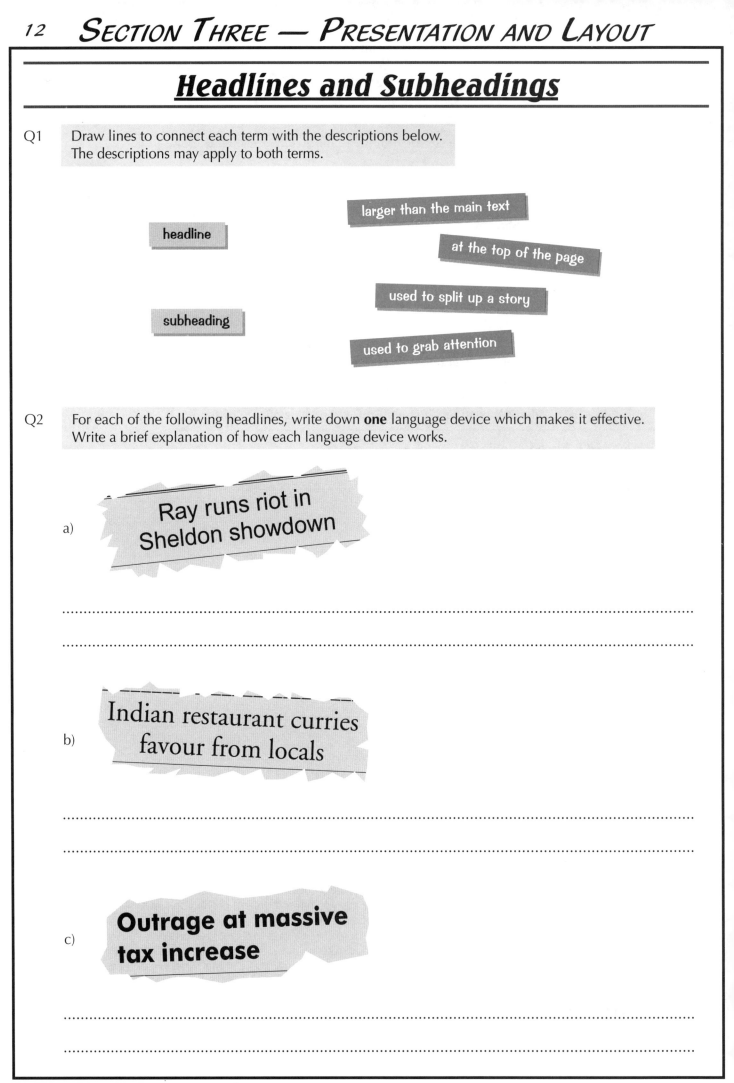

headline

larger than the main text

at the top of the page

used to split up a story

subheading

used to grab attention

Q2 For each of the following headlines, write down **one** language device which makes it effective.
Write a brief explanation of how each language device works.

a) Ray runs riot in Sheldon showdown

....

....

b) Indian restaurant curries favour from locals

....

....

c) Outrage at massive tax increase

....

....

Graphics and Captions

Q1   Briefly explain the intended purpose of each graphic and its caption.

a)   (from a newspaper article about population growth)

World population over the last 500 years

b)   (from a hotel brochure)

All our rooms are clean, comfortable and luxurious

c)   (from a political leaflet)

Your local council election candidate, Jeff Powell

a) ....

....

....

b) ....

....

....

c) ....

....

....

Q2   Read the following advertisement for the holiday destination of Montserrat. How do the headings, photographs and captions help to achieve the text's purpose?

MINI-ESSAY QUESTION

MONTSERRAT
The Emerald Isle of the Caribbean

Montserrat is a beautiful, lush, green, mountainous island, which Irish settlers named "the Emerald Isle of the Caribbean". Montserrat lies 27 miles south-west of Antigua, in the Eastern Caribbean chain of islands.

Relax on the island's idyllic, secluded beaches

Learn to dive amid beautiful unspoilt coral reefs

The beaches in Montserrat are remarkable in appearance as they have glistening black sand because of the volcanic nature of the island. They are some of the most secluded and unspoilt beaches in the world. For swimming and sunbathing they provide the most calming and leisurely experience available. The beaches also provide incomparable surroundings for diving, snorkelling, and other water sports.

For more information, go to www.visitmontserrat.com

Text Boxes and Text Columns

Q1 How does the use of columns in the following texts add to their effectiveness?

a)

Parrots under threat from pet trade

A British-based conservation organisation has warned that the future of the world's parrots is becoming severely threatened by the international trade for pets.

Thousands of parrots are captured and brought to Europe and North America each year, with many dying during the journey. Neotropical parrots have become one of the most threatened groups of birds in the world, because of international trade and also deforestation of their natural habitats.

This trend is all the more alarming, the organisation says, because until recently parrots have flourished, with numbers on the increase.

....

....

b)

Item	Was	Now	SAVING
Stanford office desk	£149.99	£99.99	33%
McIntyre Classic Dresser	£899.99	£599.99	33%
Brockwell 3-seater sofa	£750.00	£375.00	50%

....

....

Q2 Explain why you think text boxes have been used in the following examples.

a)

Energise, revitalise and relax...
...and work off those extra pounds!

Bring this document to our reception to claim your free 2-week trial voucher (valid until the end of December). You will be entitled to free gym and pool use, exercise classes, social events and loads more!

....

....

b) Here are just two examples of people who have benefited from the generosity of people like you:

Name: Oscar Luis
Age: 9
Story: Oscar used to live in a tin hut in the barrios of São Paulo. He now has clean water and basic medical services.

Name: Srinitha
Age: 7
Story: Tiny Srinitha used to beg in the train stations of Delhi. Now she lives in a modest but safe apartment with her foster parents.

....

....

Bullet Points and Numbered Lists

Q1   Explain why the use of bullet points or numbered lists is effective in the following texts.

a)

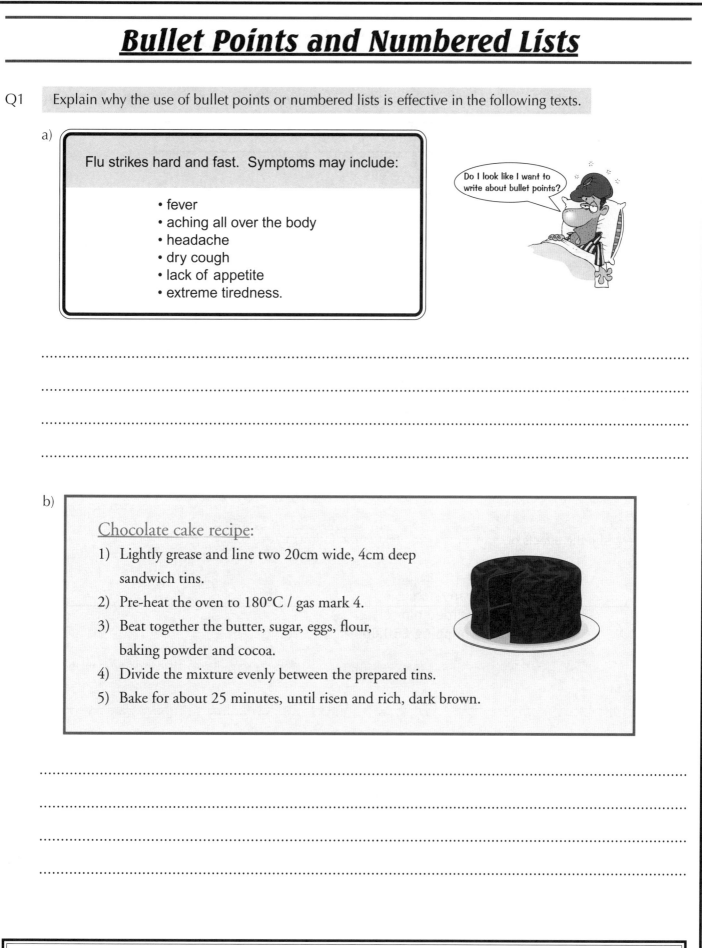

Flu strikes hard and fast. Symptoms may include:

- fever
- aching all over the body
- headache
- dry cough
- lack of appetite
- extreme tiredness.

Do I look like I want to write about bullet points?

....

....

....

....

b)

Chocolate cake recipe:

1) Lightly grease and line two 20cm wide, 4cm deep sandwich tins.

2) Pre-heat the oven to 180°C / gas mark 4.

3) Beat together the butter, sugar, eggs, flour, baking powder and cocoa.

4) Divide the mixture evenly between the prepared tins.

5) Bake for about 25 minutes, until risen and rich, dark brown.

....

....

....

....

"Interesting" is boring...

When you talk about presentational devices it's important to say <u>how</u> they work. It's no good just saying that they make the text more interesting — you have to explain their specific effects.

Font Styles and Formatting

Q1   What impression is created by the following fonts? Explain why you think each font has been used.

a) | Global warming is "worse than previously thought", say Antarctic scientists |

....

....

b) | **Looking for a great day of family fun? Give Franny's Fun Farm a ring!** |

....

....

c) | Sometimes you need to take a few risks — and don't underestimate your own abilities... |

....

....

Q2   Describe the effects of formatting of the text in the following extracts.

a)

the ... story ... day.
The failing company's chief
executive has awarded himself
a pay rise of a **whopping £50,000!**

....

....

b)

Event: World Peace Rally
Date: 15th April
Time: 7.30pm
Place: Hartnell Square

....

....

Presentation and Layout — Overview

Q1   Read the text below and then answer the question at the bottom of the page.

Eat Superfoods to Give Your Health a Boost

Change your diet and feel better than ever — we tell you how...

By Tyler Steele

If your New Year's resolution to live more healthily hasn't taken off yet, don't panic — here are some of the top "superfoods", as recommended by dieticians:

• <u>**Carrots**</u> provide beta-carotene, which can reduce the risk of stroke.

• <u>**Chilli peppers**</u> can help to reduce cholesterol and protect you from cancer.

• <u>**Tomatoes**</u> stimulate immune functions.

• <u>**Citrus fruits**</u> are an excellent source of vitamin C, which helps your body fight cancers.

Health experts are keen to point out, though, that in addition to a balanced and nutritious diet, a healthy lifestyle must also include regular exercise. A good mixture of aerobic and anaerobic exercise taken three times a week is a good general guide.

"Exercise" doesn't have to mean getting up at 5a.m. every day and running a half marathon! Something as easy as a brisk <u>30 minute walk</u> every day can make a big contribution to improved health.

Write down four presentational devices the writer uses in the leaflet and explain why they are effective.

1.   ....

....

....

2.   ....

....

....

3.   ....

....

....

4.   ....

....

....

Descriptive Language

Q1   Define the term "imagery".

....

....

Q2   For each example, identify the descriptive techniques used and say what impression they create.

a) As soon as I walked into the house, the squalid, unhygienic conditions were impossible to ignore.

....

....

b) The scruffy youth had a shock of fiery red hair, so spiky that he looked in a permanent state of surprise.

....

....

c) I remember my first football match so clearly: the sound of the fans as loud as ten jet engines; the emerald green pitch; the buzzing, electric atmosphere. I'll never forget it.

....

....

Q3   Read the text below, then answer the questions in the lovely coloured boxes.

From *Memories of Aldport*, by Geoff Buckley

I visited the old, ghostly railway bridge down the road from where I grew up. Its grey, rusty girders seemed to harbour countless memories of days gone by — the thunderous roar of an approaching train echoing down the track like a premonition of an alien invasion.

The fact that nothing passes under it any more adds to the eerie atmosphere it has now, and the strange sense of so many lives having been lived under it in the past. I would like to take a stroll along its forbidding, overgrown lines — but the combination of an unnecessary barbed wire fence and the dense, strangulating bushes surrounding the sidings sadly make this impossible.

a) How does the writer of this text feel about the railway bridge he describes?   MINI-ESSAY QUESTION

b) What writing techniques are used to describe the bridge and trains? How effective are they?

Metaphors, Similes and Analogies

Q1   Draw lines to link each term with its correct definition:

a) **metaphor**   An extended comparison where the writer describes exactly how one thing is like another.

b) **simile**   A comparison where the writer says that something is something else.

c) **analogy**   A comparison where the writer says something is similar to something else, often using the words "like" or "as".

Q2   For each phrase, say whether it is a **metaphor**, a **simile** or an **analogy**.

a) | John's as thick as two short planks. | → ....

b) | Her eyes were X-rays, penetrating my soul. | → ....

c) | An atom is similar to a solar system, with the electrons circling the nucleus in much the same way as planets orbit a star. | → ....

d) | Jane was a tower of strength. | → ....

e) | I was stuck like a lettuce in a teapot. | → ....

Q3   What impression is created by the following simile? How does it create this impression?

Jane's efforts to cheer Tom up were as fruitless as the Sahara Desert.

....

....

....

Q4   How effective is the following metaphor? Explain your answer.

His face was a snowfield of fear.

....

....

....

I know the writer quite well — I metaphor times...

Make sure you've got all these terms worked out in your head before the exam. Metaphors, similes and analogies are similar but you need to learn the differences between them.

Personification, Alliteration and Onomatopoeia

Q1   Fill in the blanks in the following sentences.

a)   .... means repeating the same sound at the start of words in a phrase.

b)   .... means describing something as if it is a person or animal.

c)   .... means a word that sounds like what it is describing.

Q2   For each extract, write down the technique being used and say what effect it creates.

a)   "The computer squawked into life before cheerily informing me I had performed an illegal operation."

....

....

....

b)   "The thumping beats on offer at the venue now are a different world from the Oompah tunes of old."

....

....

....

c)   "Bag a Bargain at Brigson's — Portsmouth's Premier Pig Farm!"

....

....

....

Q3   Read the following extract from a travel book then answer the question that follows.

> The streets of Kuala Lumpur are a labyrinth of lost lanes, back-streets, dead-ends and confusing alleys which double back on themselves. An apparently infinite series of haphazard side streets breaks out from the main street of the Chinatown area like snakes winding across the desert. On every corner hang the pungent but irresistible smells of food stalls offering a cornucopia of exotic cuisines.
>
> The low growl of heavy trucks and buzzing of the thousands of scooters that swarm the streets like bees made my dreams of a bit of peace and quiet ridiculously optimistic. The sticky heat combined with choking exhaust fumes and incessant noise certainly made for a vibrant but less than relaxing atmosphere.

MINI-ESSAY QUESTION

What writing techniques does the writer of this text use to make his descriptions vivid and effective?

Irony and Sarcasm

Q1   Briefly explain each of the following terms:

a) irony   ....

....

b) sarcasm   ....

....

c) satire   ....

....

Q2   What is the effect of the writer's sarcastic tone in this article about extending pub licensing hours?

From *Unhappy Hour* by Jane Green

Of course, the solution to binge-drinking is perfectly clear: we should keep pubs open all day long. This way, everyone will get bored of the idea of beer and take up knitting instead. I can picture it now: the young louts who terrorise our streets will surely all turn to each other and say, "Do you know what, Jeremy? This drinking lark just isn't the wheeze it used to be when we got cleared out by 11 — I'm seriously considering my life options".

....

....

....

....

....

....

Q3   How does the writer of the following extract use irony to express his opinion?   MINI-ESSAY QUESTION

From *Customer Disservice — modern day madness* by Mel Sage

   The other day I had to phone up my insurance company with the horrendously complicated problem of changing my address. After spending 20 thrilling minutes on hold listening to a variety of boy bands performing their hits, I finally got through to the man on whom my lofty ambition rested — Wayne.

   However, there was a slight hitch. It seems that, for such a highly skilled telephone operative as young Wayne, a task which to mere mortals may appear simple must be performed with studious precision. Fortunately, his professionalism shone through as he kept me informed that he was having some "technical problems". Which was obviously of great comfort to me, as I watched night time slowly approach and began to revise my plans for what was left of the week.

Technical and Emotive Language

Q1 For each language feature, fill in the box with a **T** if it's used in technical language or an **E** if it's used in emotive language.

a) statistics ☐

d) jargon ☐

b) bias ☐

e) strong opinions ☐

c) exaggeration ☐

f) rhetorical questions ☐

Q2 Find three features of emotive language in the following text, taken from a leaflet published by an environmental group. For each feature, give an example and describe what effect it creates.

> What kind of future do we want to give our children? Do we want them to have fresh air to breathe? Do we want a clean, safe environment they can enjoy and share with their own children?
>
> Or do we want a filthy, barren, concrete planet with nothing left of our once green and pleasant land, where trees are just something fondly recalled by their old, eccentric grandparents?
>
> The answer is surely obvious. Yet if we allow the situation to carry on as it is now, with mass deforestation and overdevelopment in the world's most fragile environments, we're heading for disaster. We must take action now if we have any hopes of avoiding this catastrophe.

1. ....

....

2. ....

....

3. ....

....

Q3 How does the technical language in this extract from an article about climate help the writer get information across effectively to the reader?

> The United Kingdom has a temperate maritime climate, with most lowland areas receiving between 500 and 1000mm of annual precipitation. Annual temperatures are generally between 5 and 15°C, with urban areas up to 5°C warmer than rural areas, due to the urban heat island effect. The south is also warmer than the north, due to higher levels of insolation*.

* Insolation is radiation from the sun that heats the planet.

....

....

....

....

Structure

Q1   Circle the features that you would usually expect to find in the body text of an article.

summary of the main points

opinions

headlines

separate paragraphs

bylines

specific details

statistics

Q2   The following extracts have all been taken from the same newspaper article. For each one, say whether you think it is from the **introduction**, the **body** of the article, or the **conclusion**. Explain your answers.

a)   Many motorists are in favour of the new trial scheme, seeing it as a simple, common-sense solution that will reduce the all-too-common frustration of traffic jams. But critics are concerned that, when the hard shoulder is being used for normal traffic, there will no longer be a safe place for broken down vehicles to await rescue — despite assurances that there will be regular patrols by towing vehicles to avoid accidents caused by stationary vehicles.

....

....

....

b)   The main issue is whether it can prove these worries wrong and effectively reduce congestion without adding to accident rates. If it can, it is likely to prove much more popular than other methods, such as toll roads, which are often under-used, and building extra lanes, which attracts complaints for environmental reasons. If the scheme proves successful, it could be introduced to motorways up and down the country.

....

....

....

c)   A controversial new scheme to avoid traffic congestion on one of Britain's busiest roads has divided opinion among motorists and road safety groups. The strategy, on trial from this week, allows drivers to use the hard shoulder when the amount of traffic is highest. The hard shoulder will continue to be used only for breakdowns at less busy times, with motorway signs to tell motorists when they can be used.

....

....

....

Every bit of the article is important

Although they contain less information than the body text, the introduction and conclusion are very important. The intro gets the reader's interest, and the conclusion is what will stick in their mind.

Writing Techniques — Overview

Q1   Read the text from a holiday brochure below and then answer the question at the bottom of the page.

Galápagos Islands — The 'Enchanted Isles'

The beautiful Galápagos islands are some 600 miles off the coast of Ecuador. Named after the giant tortoise which is one of their most famous residents, the Galápagos islands are probably the world's most well-preserved ecological site. This unique experience should be added to every traveller's to-do list.

For such a small and remote set of islands, the Galápagos have made an enormous contribution to science and modern thought, being the home of Darwin's finches, which formed the basis for his theory of natural selection. The overwhelming variety of animal and plant life that first attracted Darwin to these islands is still present today, with birds alone accounting for over 160 different species.

Only about 30,000 people live on the islands. The majority of the area is a protected National Park. There are thirteen larger volcanic islands which you can visit, as well as a further six smaller islands and over one hundred rocks and islets.

The sea is a sapphire of intense blue. The wildlife, which includes blue-footed boobies, flightless cormorants and marine iguanas, is as friendly and curious as a puppy. Surely the chance to see this wonderful display of flora and fauna is irresistible?

Write down four language devices the writer uses to describe the Galápagos islands and explain why they are effective.

1. ....

....

....

2. ....

....

....

3. ....

....

....

4. ....

....

....

Search and Find Questions

Q1 Look at the text below and the question that follows. Tick the box under the best exam answer, and explain why you think it is the best.

> *"Last weekend we found ourselves with nothing to do on a warm, sunny day, so decided on a trip to the zoo. The entrance to the zoo was via a rusty iron gate that looked in serious need of repair. The floor was littered with discarded crisp packets, drinks cans and revolting looking bits of burger buns. I thought things might improve once we were inside, but unfortunately I was wrong: the majority of the animals looked malnourished and miserable in their enclosures, which all seemed dull and empty with nothing for the animals to do, and precious little space for them to run around in. All in all, it was a pretty depressing place."*

A1. According to the author, why is the zoo such a "depressing place"?

a)   The writer doesn't like the way the zoo looks on the way in, and once inside he is not impressed by the animals' enclosures. It sounds like they were horrible. This made the writer regret going to the zoo.

b)   The writer is disappointed by the appearance of the zoo, referring to the "rusty iron gate" and littered floor, full of "revolting looking bits of burger buns". He is also concerned by the "dull and empty enclosures" and the "malnourished and miserable" appearance of the animals.

c)   The writer went to the zoo on a "warm, sunny day" at the weekend. They hadn't planned on going to the zoo, but had nothing else to do. Unfortunately, he wasn't impressed by the animals and the zoo entrance, describing it as a "pretty depressing place".

☐   ☐   ☐

This answer is the best because ....

....

....

Q2 Read the text below.

> I just can't understand the popularity of hip hop. Hardly any of it's original, and it's just far too easy to make. Whereas rock music involves real instruments that need skilled musicians, hip hop's created mainly on a computer, and often from recycled bits of somebody else's music. I'm not saying that anyone could do it, but I can't believe it's particularly difficult.

Born on the streets,
Harold was a rudeboy.

Write down **three phrases** from the text that would be helpful in answering the question: "Why does the writer think that rock music is better than hip hop?"

1. ....

2. ....

3. ....

P.E.E.

Q1 In an exam answer, which of the following could you **not** use as an example to back up a point? Circle the correct answer.

 a) A quote from the text.

 c) Your opinion of the text.

 b) A fact or statistic from the text.

 d) A description of the presentation of the text.

Q2 Read the following exam answers. Tick the answers which use the P.E.E. technique (Point, Example, Explanation).

a) The writer uses similes to make his description of Kidston's motor racing more vivid. For example, he describes Kidston's Bentley as being "like a cheetah". This shows how powerful and fast Kidston's car was.

b) The writer says the racing driver Glen Kidston was glamorous and charismatic. He had an affair with the young Barbara Cartland. In 1931, he died tragically in a plane crash in the Drakensberg Mountains.

c) The writer uses the headline of the magazine article to capture readers' attention. It describes Glen Kidston as "Britain's Forgotten Hero". This sounds glamorous and mysterious and would intrigue readers.

☐ ☐ ☐

Q3 Read the following extract from a tourist information sheet and answer the question which follows.

Avebury Visitor Centre: Information Sheet 5
West Kennet Long Barrow

West Kennet Long Barrow is an ancient chambered tomb near Avebury. There are five chambers (rooms) in the tomb. It is safe to go inside the tomb to look at the chambers. When the tomb was excavated, different types of skeleton were found in each chamber:
• Male adult skeletons were found in the main chamber, opposite the entrance.
• Children's skeletons were found in the chamber to the left of the entrance.
• The skeletons of elderly people were found in the chamber to the right of the entrance.
• A mixture of male and female adult skeletons were found in the two other chambers.

Explain how the writer has used a presentational device to make the text more effective. Use the P.E.E. framework below to help you answer the question.

Point ....

....

Example ....

....

Explanation ....

....

....

So much better than freestyle waffling...

P.E.E. gives you a framework for answering exam questions well. Making points without backing them up is like making beans on toast without beans. And that's no good. No good at all.

Writing in Paragraphs

Q1   Circle the words and phrases which would be useful for linking paragraphs together.

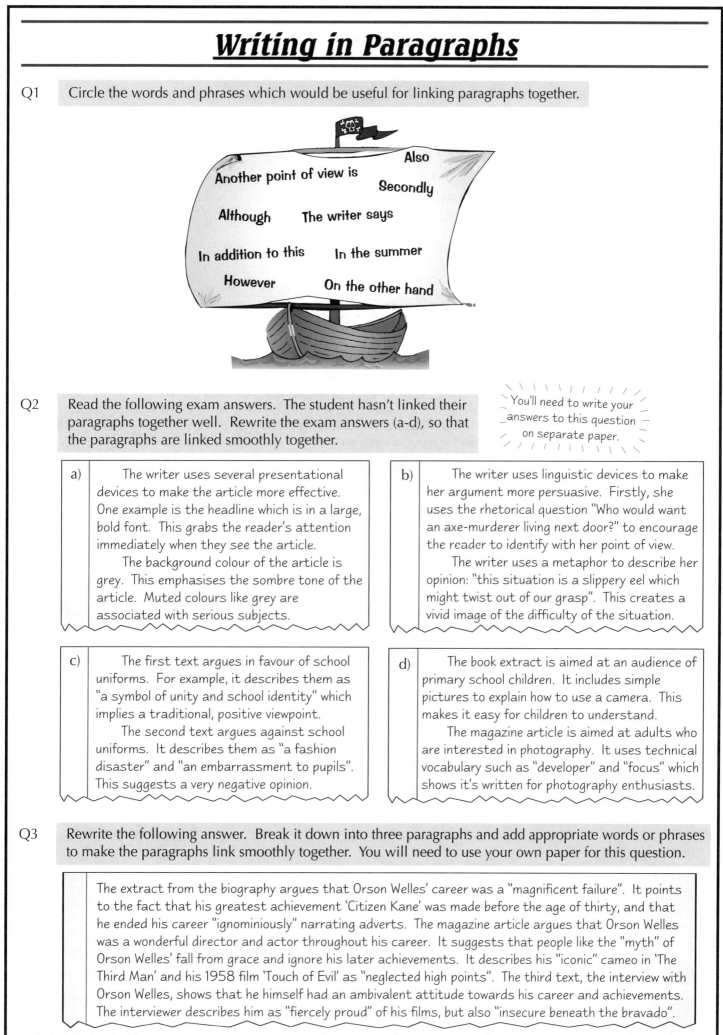

Another point of view is

Also

Secondly

Although   The writer says

In addition to this   In the summer

However   On the other hand

Q2   Read the following exam answers. The student hasn't linked their paragraphs together well. Rewrite the exam answers (a-d), so that the paragraphs are linked smoothly together.

You'll need to write your answers to this question on separate paper.

a)   The writer uses several presentational devices to make the article more effective. One example is the headline which is in a large, bold font. This grabs the reader's attention immediately when they see the article.
    The background colour of the article is grey. This emphasises the sombre tone of the article. Muted colours like grey are associated with serious subjects.

b)   The writer uses linguistic devices to make her argument more persuasive. Firstly, she uses the rhetorical question "Who would want an axe-murderer living next door?" to encourage the reader to identify with her point of view.
    The writer uses a metaphor to describe her opinion: "this situation is a slippery eel which might twist out of our grasp". This creates a vivid image of the difficulty of the situation.

c)   The first text argues in favour of school uniforms. For example, it describes them as "a symbol of unity and school identity" which implies a traditional, positive viewpoint.
    The second text argues against school uniforms. It describes them as "a fashion disaster" and "an embarrassment to pupils". This suggests a very negative opinion.

d)   The book extract is aimed at an audience of primary school children. It includes simple pictures to explain how to use a camera. This makes it easy for children to understand.
    The magazine article is aimed at adults who are interested in photography. It uses technical vocabulary such as "developer" and "focus" which shows it's written for photography enthusiasts.

Q3   Rewrite the following answer. Break it down into three paragraphs and add appropriate words or phrases to make the paragraphs link smoothly together. You will need to use your own paper for this question.

The extract from the biography argues that Orson Welles' career was a "magnificent failure". It points to the fact that his greatest achievement 'Citizen Kane' was made before the age of thirty, and that he ended his career "ignominiously" narrating adverts. The magazine article argues that Orson Welles was a wonderful director and actor throughout his career. It suggests that people like the "myth" of Orson Welles' fall from grace and ignore his later achievements. It describes his "iconic" cameo in 'The Third Man' and his 1958 film 'Touch of Evil' as "neglected high points". The third text, the interview with Orson Welles, shows that he himself had an ambivalent attitude towards his career and achievements. The interviewer describes him as "fiercely proud" of his films, but also "insecure beneath the bravado".

Reading with Insight

Q1   Draw lines to match up each sentence (a-d) with the type of tone it conveys (i-iv).

a) I was disgusted by the badly researched, shabby journalism
    displayed by your newspaper's coverage of the event.

b) The MP Gareth Soames visited the County Hospital on
    Thursday 11th December to open a new ward.

c) Gary Barlow's dancing drew gasps of wonder from the
    crowd — the rumours were true, he really had improved!

d) There's nothing I love more than queueing in a really long
    traffic jam on a boiling hot day — it's fantastic.

i)   **light-hearted tone**

ii) **sarcastic tone**

iii) **serious tone**

iv) **angry tone**

Q2   Read the following text and answer the questions which follow.

> The films Alfred Hitchcock made in the 1950s and 1960s contain glimpses of greatness. Iconic images from these films have entered popular culture, for example Janet Leigh screaming in the shower in 'Psycho'.
>
> However, when looking at Hitchcock's career as a whole, it is his earlier films from the 1930s and 1940s which still delight. Early movies like 'The 39 Steps' and 'The Lady Vanishes' have a wonderful humour, paciness and lightness of touch. In contrast, his later films, even classics like 'Vertigo' and 'The Birds', are often leaden in their pace and tone.
>
> One reason for the change in quality of Hitchcock's films was the way he started to be treated as a prestigious, "auteur" director as he got older. Younger film directors like François Truffaut idolised him. This swelled Hitchcock's already substantial ego, and contributed to an increasingly pretentious style of film-making. Stories from the 1950s and 1960s about his bullying, possessive attitude towards young actresses like Tippi Hedren, also raise doubts about his professionalism in his later years.
>
> So my advice is: settle down on the sofa to watch some of those early, off-the-cuff, Hitchcock masterpieces — and leave the later "classics" for nerdy film students.

a) Pick out words and phrases from the text to complete the table below.

Question 2
take 2

Words and phrases which imply the writer dislikes Hitchcock's later films	Words and phrases which imply the writer likes Hitchcock's early films	Words and phrases which imply the writer dislikes Hitchcock as a person
1.	1.	1.
2.	2.	2.

b) How does the tone of the text change in the last paragraph?

    ....

    ....

    ....

c) In this text, the writer describes his enthusiasm for Alfred Hitchcock's early films. Describe something
    you feel enthusiastic about — and explain how this helps you understand the writer's feelings.

    ....

    ....

    ....

Comparing Texts

Q1   Read the following two texts and answer the questions which follow.

Linda's Problem Page — answers your most embarrassing problems!!!

I farted in front of him!
Dear Linda,
There's a boy at school I really like. He sat next to me in a Maths lesson and I was really excited cos I thought he might fancy me. But I farted and he hasn't talked to me since. What can I do? Love Zoe xxxxx

Linda says....
Hi Zoe,
Oops! How embarrassing! Don't worry though. Silly moments like this happen to all of us. If this boy really likes you, he won't let one fart get in the way of a relationship. My advice is: be confident, and go and talk to him next time you see him. You'll both soon forget all about it. Good luck! Linda.

Write to Linda c/o 'Girl!' magazine, PO Box 5058

Personal Financial Advice: Case Study

Case Study: Ms Barber, 35, single, no dependants
Salary: £18,000 per annum
Savings: £14,500 in an ISA, 3.5% interest
Pension: Contributes 8% of her salary to a private stakeholder pension.
Property: 1 bed flat, mortgage £290/month.
Debt: Credit card debt £2100, 9% APR

The Daily Missive's financial advisor, Greg Smith writes Ms Barber should pay off her credit card debt using part of her ISA savings. She's currently paying more interest on her credit card debt than she is earning on her ISA.

Secondly, Ms Barber should find out whether her employer would be prepared to make contributions to her pension, which would improve her pension fund.

Finally, Ms Barber should move her ISA to a different bank or building society. 3.5% isn't a competitive rate of interest for an ISA. She should aim for 4.5%.

a)   Complete the following table with notes about the two texts.

	Linda's Problem Page	Personal Financial Advice
Audience of text		
Purpose of text		
Tone of text		
Main language devices used		
Main presentational devices used		

b)   Compare how each text uses language and presentational devices.

MINI-ESSAY QUESTION

Aah, farting in Maths lessons... Those were the days...

You're rattling through the book now — only the exam section left to go. Don't worry about that — it might look like a tiger, but it's really just a harmless tabby cat. Ahh.

Section Five — Exam Techniques

Sample Exam — Questions

In this section, <u>you</u> get to be the <u>examiner</u>. You'll look at some students' answers to exam questions and <u>decide what marks</u> they should get. It'll help you understand what examiners are looking for — which will improve the quality of your own answers. Here's how it works:

1) <u>Read</u> the sample exam questions and texts on pages 30-33. They're similar in style to the ones you'll get in <u>Paper 2, Section A</u> of your GCSE English exam. Make sure you understand the questions and texts. You <u>don't</u> have to answer the questions.

2) Then on pages 34-41 there are <u>mark schemes</u> explaining <u>how to mark</u> each question. And there are some <u>student answers</u> which you have to mark.

Here are the sample exam questions. Remember — <u>this time</u>, you don't have to answer the questions. Phew.

Look at 'Eyewitness', an advertisement for the medical charity Médecins Sans Frontières.

A1 Read the first five paragraphs, up to "… and, at the moment, a lot of malaria."

What impression does the advertisement give of Meriel Rosser's work in these paragraphs? You must use the text to support your answer.

[10 marks]

A2 Read the final three paragraphs, starting from "Darfur is a tough place to work…"

According to Rosser, what are the major challenges involved in working in Darfur? What attitudes does she express towards her work?

[10 marks]

Now look at the article 'Voluntary work abroad' from the British Government Website.

A3 How effective is the writer in encouraging the reader to take part in voluntary work abroad?

[10 marks]

To answer this question you will need to look at the advertisement and the article.

A4 Compare the impressions of working abroad given by the Médecins Sans Frontières advertisement and the British Government website article.

You should consider:

- the purpose of each text;
- the use of language and style in each text;
- the organisation and structure of each text.

[10 marks]

And tonight Matthew — I will be The Examiner...

Enjoy being an examiner while you can. Cherish the feeling of power... Buy a red pen... On p.42 your examiner status will be taken away and you'll have to answer the questions again. Drat.

Sample Exam — Text

Here's the first text for the exam questions on page 30. It's an advert for the medical charity Médecins Sans Frontières (MSF). Give it a read through.

EYEWITNESS

© Kadir van Lohuizen

Meriel Rosser from the UK has volunteered for MSF in many countries around the world, but she just can't help returning to Sudan. Here she describes the ongoing crisis in Darfur. Although media coverage of the region has declined, the situation has still not improved for the millions of people caught up in the conflict there.

MSF volunteer Meriel Rosser delivers a message from the frontline.

"It is 2.20 am and 34 degrees C... Welcome to Khartoum!" I seem to be attached to a piece of elastic that keeps bouncing me back to Sudan since my first stint here some three years ago. Then I was in charge of MSF's work treating the deadly disease kala azar (also know as visceral leishmaniasis) in Gedaref state in the east of the country.

Now I'm in the west in Darfur, where the fighting that has been going on here over the last three years has had

terrible consequences for the people.

I'm based in Muhajariya, a heartland of the Sudan Liberation Army. MSF is trying to meet some of the huge needs that have arisen because people have fled their homes and because basic necessities like water and sanitation and especially medical services are so limited. During the time we have worked in Darfur we have been providing nutritional support to malnourished children and running a field hospital carrying out surgery for Caesarean sections, as well as injuries related to the ongoing violence, such as gunshot wounds. We also run clinics where we provide primary health care and see people affected by diarrhoea, fever and, at the moment, a lot of malaria.

Darfur is a tough place to work, and the medical needs remain enormous. Violence against civilians continues and people are forced to flee their homes repeatedly. Getting enough food and other humanitarian support is a continuous battle.

We have dealt with births, deaths (always too many, but we know there are many more we save), reports of

Dengue fever in the next state, rabies cases around Darfur... the challenges are endless. Although it's not easy, I do sometimes look around and think that I'm lucky to be in a position to experience this – the beautiful smiling faces of children, the graceful herders on their camels and the waves from people going about their everyday business. And I'm even luckier to be part of an organisation that can really do something to help the most vulnerable.

We are able to do that because people like you support our work. You allow us to react quickly and independently. I am continually amazed at just how much we can do thanks to you.

" Just because Darfur is not in the news as much as it was a year or so ago does not mean that the situation for individuals living the nightmare has improved at all. "
Meriel Rosser, MSF volunteer, Darfur, Sudan

(Above image) April 4, 2006: Kalma camp, Darfur, women patiently wait to be seen by an MSF doctor. The health of women is a particular concern because they have to shoulder the burden of taking care of huge families without resources or support. This leaves many exhausted and vulnerable to illness.

MEDECINS SANS FRONTIERES

ENGLISH CHARITY REGISTRATION NUMBER 1026588

To help MSF with a monthly donation, please go to www.uk.msf.org/support EMC2

Sample Exam — Text

And here's the second text for the exam. It's an article from the British Government website.

Voluntary work abroad

 **Ever wanted to combine travelling with making a difference? Through volunteering abroad you could do both. Wherever your skills and experience lie and whatever your interests, there is likely to be a project suited to you.**

From animal and environmental projects to helping rebuild communities that have been destroyed by an earthquake, giving even a few weeks of your time will bring real benefits to the area and the people that live there. Through volunteering in another country you can also broaden your horizons, learn about a different culture and make new friends.

Volunteers come from all walks of life including homeworkers, students during a gap year, teachers, engineers, health workers, scientists and government officers.

International experience, in the workplace or as a volunteer, also adds another interesting dimension to your CV and can make your job or promotion application stand out.

Volunteering opportunities on offer

Organisations like the British Council, Voluntary Services Overseas (VSO) and charities with international units can help you make a decision about volunteering abroad and find the right project for you. The Year Out Group also has information on a range of volunteering opportunities.

> take time to find a project that suits you

The British Council's Connect Youth offers programmes ranging from group exchanges to individual voluntary service, designed to give young people an international experience.

The VSO is an international development charity, which tries to match people's skills and professional background to the need for volunteers across the world. The ages of its volunteers range from 17 to 75.

If there is a particular charity or voluntary organisation you would like to help, contact it to find out if it needs any volunteers to work overseas.

The first volunteering project you find is not necessarily going to be ideally suited to you, but it is worth looking until you discover something you would feel comfortable doing.

Sample Exam — Text

Talk to the organisers of the volunteer programme about any concerns and check what safety measures are in place, as well as what would happen if you had to return to the UK earlier than you had expected or you find the project is not for you.

Taking a career break from your job

If you are in paid employment, find out how taking a career break or secondment to volunteer abroad would affect your work contract, health cover, pension and national insurance contributions, as well as your continued service.

Some employers will have a policy to encourage their staff to take part in volunteering or see a community project they are sponsoring abroad. Others may consider counting your volunteering period as extended leave without pay or as a secondment - this could be helpful if you are considering volunteering abroad for a long period.

If you expect to return to your job at the end of your volunteering period, give your employer your contact details and the name of the organisation you are volunteering through in case they need to contact you urgently or update you about developments in the firm.

Before you go

Make sure you have the vaccinations you need for the country and check if there is any travel safety advice from the Foreign and Commonwealth Office.

You will need a valid passport to cover the entire period you will be overseas. It is also worth finding out the contact details and location of the British Consul in the country where you will be working (see the related links on this page).

The organisation you will be working through may have travel and health insurance to cover you while you are abroad. Check what you are covered for and if you need to take out any additional policies.

While you are away, try and keep regular contact with the charity or organisation you are volunteering through and make sure they know where to find you in case of an emergency. This will help you find out about any changes in the country that may affect your safety or health. If you are concerned about the situation in a country, keep in contact with the British consul in the area.

Wherever you choose to volunteer, enjoy the experience as it can be fun as well as rewarding.

www.direct.gov.uk © Crown Copyright

Mark Scheme — Question A1

This page gives you <u>advice and a mark scheme</u> for marking question A1 of the sample exam.
Read this information and digest it. Then you'll be ready for marking the student answers on p.35.

Question A1 is about impressions

1) This question tells you to "use the text to support your answer". So a good answer will be backed up by quotes and examples from the text.

2) You have about 10 minutes to write each answer in the exam — so good answers don't have to be very long. Half a side or so will do.

Jon's impression of a tree always went down well at parties.

Look for good points like these when you're marking

If a student's written good points like these in their answer, they're on track for a good mark...

- Rosser treated the "deadly disease kala azar", so her work sounds both dangerous and important.
- She says she was "in charge of MSF's work" so she seems to be in a position of responsibility.
- The advertisement gives the impression that Rosser's work is vitally important, as she says "we provide primary health care".
- It mentions extreme conditions, e.g. when it's "2.20 a.m. and 34 degrees C", so her work environment doesn't sound comfortable.
- Her text is described as "a message from the frontline", so it sounds like she is working in a hazardous area.

There are plenty of other good points that could get marks — these are just suggestions.

Use this mark scheme to mark question A1

Look at the table below to see what an <u>answer needs to be like</u> to gain each mark. Each row of descriptions is for a <u>range</u> of possible marks (e.g. 2–4 marks). If the answer does <u>everything</u> in the description, and does it well, give it a mark from the top end of the range. If the answer doesn't do everything, but does do <u>some of it</u>, give it a mark from the bottom end of the range.

Mark	Quality of Answer
0 marks	Nothing written that helps to answer the question.
1 mark	Simple comments with a few references to the text, or just copying unselectively.
2–4 marks	Simple comments about the main features of the text. Some attempt to explain the content of the advertisement.
5–7 marks	Selects, and begins to analyse, appropriate information from the text about Meriel Rosser's work. Sensible, valid comments based on the text.
8–10 marks	Appropriate selection and analysis of details from the text, showing insight and an assured understanding of the impressions created of Meriel Rosser's work.

A good mark — like that nice lad from Take That...

The mark scheme might look a bit scary at first — but give it a read through and you'll see it's common sense really. The better the answer, the better the mark. It ain't rocket science.

Sample Answers — Question A1

Now it's your turn to be the <u>examiner</u>. This can be <u>tricky</u> but it's really <u>useful</u> if you can do it.

1) Make sure you've read the advice and mark scheme on page 34.
2) Use the mark scheme to <u>mark</u> the answers to question A1 below.
3) <u>Explain</u> how you've decided on the marks in the lines below the answers.
4) The <u>first one's been done for you</u> to show you what to do.

Write notes around the answer — that's what the real examiners do.

> **A1** Read the first five paragraphs, up to "… and, at the moment, a lot of malaria."
>
> What impression does the advertisement give of Meriel Rosser's work in these paragraphs? You must use the text to support your answer.
>
> [10 marks]

Answer 1

A1   The advert says that Meriel Rosser "has volunteered for MSF in many countries across the world," which gives the impression that she travels a lot for her work. She seems to love working in Sudan so much that "she just can't help returning".

However, she also says that it is 34 degrees C at 2.20 am and that she is working where fighting is going on in "a heartland of the Sudan Liberation Army" — which makes it sound as though she works in extreme and dangerous conditions. She mentions that she was "in charge" of treating a deadly disease, so her job sounds important, and it also sounds like her work is vital because she is working to feed "malnourished children" and to help with "injuries".

This answer gets [9] marks out of 10 because ...*it is thorough and includes several relevant pieces of evidence. It is clearly written and shows good understanding of the text.*

Answer 2

A1   I get the impression that Meriel Rosser enjoys her work because it says she keeps coming back to Sudan. She was in charge of MSF's work, so must have been important. Her work sounds dangerous because there has been fighting where she works and it has been terrible for the people there. Her work is about helping people who are starving or have been injured. She also helps people with diseases and helps to run a clinic.

This answer gets [ ] marks out of 10 because ....

....

....

....

....

Section Six — Sample Exam

Mark Scheme — Question A2

Here's advice and a mark scheme for marking question A2. Read all this info through — then you'll be prepared for marking the sample student answers on the next page.

Question A2 is really two questions

1) This question is in two parts. A good answer should respond to both parts equally.
2) But there's no need for an answer to address the two parts of the question separately. If a quote from the text is relevant to both parts of the question, then it's fine to talk about them both at once.
3) Good answers will use evidence from the text to support their points.

Look for good points like these when you're marking

These are the kinds of points you'd find in a good answer to the question...

The major challenges of working in Darfur

- Darfur is "a tough place to work", but the work needs to be done — even though it puts the volunteers themselves at risk due to "violence against civilians".
- There is a wide range of complicated work to do, and "the challenges are endless", including "births, deaths, reports of Dengue fever..."
- The challenges are ongoing, for example "getting enough food and other humanitarian support is a continuous battle." The word "battle" emphasises the difficulty.

Meriel Rosser's attitude towards her work

- Meriel Rosser loves her job, commenting that she's "lucky".
- She recognises the beauty in her surroundings, e.g. "the beautiful, smiling faces of children, the graceful herders on their camels", and sees her time in Sudan as a precious experience.
- She is "continually amazed" at how much her charity can achieve thanks to the people who donate to MSF.

Mark question A2 like this

Here's the mark scheme table for question A2.

Mark	Quality of Answer
0 marks	Nothing written that helps to answer the question.
1 mark	Simple comments with no clear links to the question, or some unselective copying from the text.
2–4 marks	Simple comments, mainly written in the student's own words with some attempt to explain the challenges facing Rosser and her attitude towards them. Uses some evidence from the text.
5–7 marks	Clear comments on the different challenges facing Rosser and her attitude towards them. Quotations or examples are used, and their meaning is explained.
8–10 marks	Detailed and valid commentary on the text showing excellent understanding of the challenges and Meriel's attitude. Details from the text are used to support the answer. Points are well-arranged and coherent.

Sample Answers — Question A2

Now it's time to have a go at marking answers to question A2. Don't be too merciless...

1) Read the mark scheme on page 36.

2) Use this mark scheme to <u>mark</u> the answers below to question A2.

3) Then <u>explain</u> why you gave those marks in the lines below the answers.

It's how you explain your marking that's the important bit.

A2 Read the final three paragraphs, starting from "Darfur is a tough place to work…"

According to Rosser, what are the major challenges involved in working in Darfur? What attitudes does she express towards her work?

[10 marks]

Answer 1

A2   Darfur is a tough place to work and people have to flee their homes a lot because of all the fighting and there is not enough food. There are a lot of challenges because it says that the challenges are endless. Her attitude is that she is lucky because she works for MSF and she is lucky to be a member of that organisation because it can really do something to help.

This answer gets [ ] marks out of 10 because ....

....

....

....

....

Answer 2

A2   Meriel Rosser says that Darfur is "tough" which makes it sound as though working there is difficult. She writes about "violence against civilians" and "people forced to flee" — which must make it a scary place to work, and one where it is hard to keep track of patients. She also writes that they have to deal with "births, deaths", "reports of Dengue fever" and "rabies", which is a large range of problems.
    Even though the challenges are big, Rosser still thinks she is "lucky" to do her work — she mentions "beautiful" children and "graceful herders on their camels". This makes it seem that she is enjoying having experiences that other people don't normally have. She is also grateful to people who give money, saying she is "amazed" at what they can do.

This answer gets [ ] marks out of 10 because ....

....

....

....

....

Mark Scheme — Question A3

Hopefully you'll be getting the hang of it by now. Read through the advice and mark scheme on this page, then mark the answers on p.39.

Question A3 is asking you for a personal opinion

1) This type of question wants to know your opinion.

2) A good answer still needs some quotations from the text, but this time they'll be to <u>justify</u> opinions rather than to directly answer the question.

3) Comments on <u>structure</u>, <u>presentation and language</u> or anything else that could influence an opinion of the effectiveness of the article are all relevant.

Pointy hats, claws, sabres, horns and teeth get 0 marks.

Look for good points like these when you're marking

- The article opens with a question — "ever wanted to combine travelling with making a difference?" This is effective in making the reader think about any previous times they've considered working abroad.

- The first paragraph is printed in bold and addresses the reader directly. It builds a rapport with the reader and encourages them to read the whole article.

- The article tells the reader that "your time will bring real benefits", so it makes it sound like they can make a difference.

- The subheadings aren't very persuasive — they're just plain and informative, e.g. "Volunteering opportunities on offer".

- By advising people in jobs to find out how a career break "would affect your work contract, health cover, pension and national insurance contributions, as well as your continued service", the article makes taking voluntary work sound difficult to arrange. This is likely to make the article less persuasive.

Remember — these are just suggestions.

Mark question A3 like this

The table below describes what an answer needs to be like to get each mark.

Mark	Quality of Answer
0 marks	Nothing written that helps to answer the question.
1 mark	Some simple comments, possibly with unselective copying of text from the article. Answer not clearly linked to the question.
2–4 marks	Some simple comments on the effectiveness of the article. Shows some awareness of persuasive techniques.
5–7 marks	Some valid comments on the effectiveness of the article, backed up by evidence from the text. Clear focus on persuasive techniques.
8–10 marks	Valid and well-argued comments on the effectiveness of the text. Points are linked together coherently and details from the text are used to back up answer throughout.

Sample Answers — Question A3

More marking for you to do on this page. Remember to write "v.g." on the good answers...

1) Read the mark scheme on page 38.

2) Use this mark scheme to <u>mark</u> these answers to question A3.

3) Then <u>explain</u> why you gave those marks in the lines below the answers.

> **A3** How effective is the writer in encouraging the reader to take part in voluntary work abroad?
>
> [10 marks]

Answer 1

A3   The article starts off by asking a rhetorical question and then says that there is likely to be a project suited to you to make you think that being an overseas volunteer would be a good thing. It says that you can help lots of projects and that you can "broaden your horizons, learn about a different culture and make new friends". It says that volunteers can come "in all shapes and sizes" and that might encourage people because it is saying that anyone can help. It also says that you are able to find help to become a volunteer and it tells you about the British Council and other organisations. At the end of the article it tells you that you need to check with your employer before you volunteer and this might put some people off. At the end of the article it tells you that the experience would be fun.

This answer gets [ ] marks out of 10 because ....

....

....

....

....

Answer 2

A3   The text is very effective because it tells you a lot about volunteering abroad. It tells you about the types of places that you can go and work and it says that it can be fun. It also gives you lots of helpful information about where you can go to get help. It tells you that you need to have vaccinations before you go abroad and this is because overseas countries have diseases. Overall, I think that this leaflet is very effective and it would make me want to go abroad to volunteer.

This answer gets [ ] marks out of 10 because ....

....

....

....

....

Mark Scheme — Question A4

This is the last question on the exam paper — and the <u>hardest</u>. Read through this page to find out what a good answer needs to be like.

Question A4 asks for a comparison

1) Comparing texts means looking for <u>differences</u> as well as <u>similarities</u>.

2) The <u>bullet points</u> tell you what the examiner is looking for — good answers should cover all of the bullets.

3) Good answers are likely to have an <u>equal</u> amount written about each article.

The similarities were obvious.

Look for good points like these when you're marking

• The purpose of the MSF advert is to persuade the reader to "help MSF with a monthly donation". This purpose is made clear in the text at the bottom of the page. This text is in a box and in a larger font to make it stand out. The purpose of the government article, on the other hand, is both to advise and persuade. It gives advice about volunteering abroad, for example under the subheading "Before you go". However, it also persuades the reader to volunteer, by emphasising the benefits, for example saying "you can also broaden your horizons."

• The MSF advert portrays working abroad as a worthwhile but difficult challenge. A metaphor is used to describe the work as "a continuous battle" which emphasises how hard it is. In contrast, the government article emphasises positive points about working abroad to encourage people to volunteer, for example saying that it will be "fun" and that you can "make new friends".

• The MSF advert starts like a news report, making it feel immediate and dramatic. It ends with a request for donations, to leave that thought present in reader's minds. The government text, on the other hand, is divided into sections with informative headings that make it suitable for use as a reference text. It gives a less emotional account of working abroad. But it ends with a positive message that is likely to make people feel encouraged to volunteer.

Mark question A4 like this

Mark	Quality of Answer
0 marks	Nothing written that helps to answer the question.
1 mark	Not much written, and not clearly linked to the question. Unselective copying of the texts.
2–4 marks	Simple comments on the texts, with some basic comparisons. Some evidence used from the texts. May not cover all the bullet points for both texts.
5–7 marks	Some valid comparisons of the texts, with evidence from both texts used to back up points. Answer is fairly well organised and coherent.
8–10 marks	Confident and well-organised answer with a range of valid comparisons between the texts, linked together coherently. Quotations used to back up all significant points. Covers all the bullet points.

Sample Answers — Question A4

This is your final page of marking. Then everything's back to normal in section 7.

1) Read the mark scheme and advice on page 40.

2) Use this mark scheme to <u>mark</u> these answers to question A4.

3) Then <u>explain</u> why you gave those marks in the lines below the answers.

> **A4** Compare the impressions of working abroad given by the Médecins Sans Frontières advertisement and the British Government website article.
>
> You should consider:
>
> • the purpose of each text;
> • the use of language and style in each text;
> • the organisation and structure of each text. [10 marks]

Answer 1

A4   The MSF advert tries to persuade people to donate money. It has information at the bottom showing how you can make a monthly donation. The government article is also trying to persuade people, but to volunteer for work abroad, not to give money.

The language in the MSF advert is mostly formal and uses words such as "malnourished" to show what has happened to the children. The government article is also formal because it's from the government, but the MSF advert is more emotional — for example when it says "I am continually amazed at just how much we can do".

The MSF advert is organised into columns like a newspaper, which might help to make it more believable. The Government article looks more like an information leaflet so people might trust it more.

This answer gets [ ] marks out of 10 because ....

....

....

....

....

Answer 2

A4   Both of the texts aim to persuade. The advertisement wants the reader "to help MSF with a monthly donation" whereas the article wants to persuade people that volunteering abroad is helpful because "there is likely to be a project suited to you". The purpose of the advertisement is to tell the reader what it is actually like to be a volunteer, for example when it says "I sometimes think I'm lucky", but the government article just advises you where to find information on volunteering.

This answer gets [ ] marks out of 10 because ....

....

....

....

....

Practice Exam — Questions

Here are some practice exam questions for 'Reading non-fiction and media texts'. They're similar in style to the ones you'll get in <u>Paper 2, Section A</u> of your GCSE English exam.

To make it more like the real exam, do <u>all the questions</u> in one go, and give yourself <u>50 minutes</u> to answer them. Try to use everything you've learnt so far about what makes a good exam answer...

The Resource Material for these questions is a newspaper article 'Climate change brings Eiger to earth' by Steven Swinford, and a book extract, 'The Beckoning Silence', by Joe Simpson.

Look at the newspaper article 'Climate change brings Eiger to earth'.

A1 According to the writer, Steven Swinford, how is climate change having an effect on mountains in the Alps and the people who use them?   [10 marks]

Now look at the first three paragraphs of 'The Beckoning Silence' by Joe Simpson.

A2 What impression does the writer, Joe Simpson, give of the Eiger mountain in these paragraphs? You must use the text to support your answer.   [10 marks]

Now consider the whole extract by Joe Simpson.

A3 What is Joe Simpson's attitude towards climbing the north face of the Eiger mountain?
   [10 marks]

To answer this question you will need to look at both texts.

A4 Compare the impressions of mountains and mountaineering given by the extract and the article. You should organise your answer into three paragraphs using the following headings:
   • the impressions of the Eiger;
   • the impessions of the mountaineers;
   • the impressions of the tourists.   [10 marks]

Practice Exams — the most fun you can have...

Okay, maybe not. But they're incredibly useful. One guy I went to school with never did a practice exam in his life, and he now lives in a sewer. And, ummm, he often gets bitten by rats.

Practice Exam — Text

Here's the first text to go with the practice exam questions on page 42. It's a newspaper article from the Sunday Times.

July 9, 2006

Climate change brings Eiger to earth by Steven Swinford

A SLAB of rock weighing millions of tons is poised to break away from the Eiger, one of Europe's most treacherous mountains, and crash into the valley below, a geologist has warned. Hans-Rudolf Keusen, who monitors the Bernese Alps for the Swiss government, said 2m cubic metres of the Eiger mountain are set to collapse, in what would be Europe's biggest rock fall for 15 years. The limestone slab is equivalent in volume to two Empire State Buildings. "It will be a spectacular sight," said Keusen. "There aren't any houses underneath, so nobody is going to get hit by a rock on the head." Keusen first spotted the fissure between the limestone slab and the rockface at the beginning of June. It measured 8in then, but has since widened to just over 16ft and is growing at a rate of 35in a day. According to Keusen, the crack has been caused by the retreat of the Grindelwald glacier, which previously supported the rockface. As it has shrunk, holes in the limestone have opened and been eroded by water. He said: "In the past 25 years the glacier has regressed very quickly, by up to a metre a year. We believe this accelerated regression is the result of climate change. Without the support of the glacier, small fissures have opened in the rock which have widened significantly. This is happening very fast, and the rock could fall within days."

In the past week tourists have been gathering in the nearby town of Grindelwald in the hope of catching the dramatic collapse, which will see 5m tons of limestone fall over 650ft. The rockfall will not pose a direct threat to the nearby community, but Keusen said debris could settle on glaciers, blocking water flowing out of them and affecting water supplies.

For climbers, the Eiger, 13,025ft high, has long held a special resonance. Its treacherous north face was first climbed by Heinrich Harrer in 1938, the pioneering Austrian mountaineer who later sparked controversy when he became a member of the SS. The mountain was also the setting for the 1975 Clint Eastwood film, The Eiger Sanction. According to Doug Scott, the first Briton to conquer the summit of Everest, the Alps are now more dangerous than ever: "In the past few years the alpine climbs like the Dru and the Eiger have become more and more threatened by snowfall and massive collapses. I first climbed the Alps in 1957, but they are far more dangerous today."

While it is natural for the Alps to erode, there is growing evidence that they are collapsing at a faster rate. Two years ago three lumps of the Dolomites in northern Italy came loose, with one 250ft chunk falling more than a quarter of a mile and landing on a hikers' trail. According to Professor Michael Davies of Dundee University, a civil engineer and member of the International Permafrost Association, the increased rockfalls are occurring because the permafrost that stabilises the surface of the Alps is melting.

There are also concerns that climate change will have an impact on tourism. A study for the United Nations environment programme predicted that half of all ski resorts in the Alps could be forced out of business in the next 25 years by rising temperatures.

Dr Rolf Bürki, who led the project, said: "Climate change will have the effect of pushing winter sports higher and higher up the mountains, concentrating impacts in ever-decreasing areas. As ski resorts in lower altitudes face bankruptcy, so the pressure on highly environmentally sensitive upper-altitude areas rises."

Practice Exam — Text

Here's the second text for the exam questions on page 40. It's an extract from a non-fiction book.

The Beckoning Silence
by Joe Simpson

The Eiger is part of the northern bulwark of the Alps which is prone to sudden savage storms, frequently generated by the powerful warm *Föhn* winds, often prolonged and lethal. In an instant the face becomes a maelstrom of avalanches, waterfalls and falling rocks, cutting off all hope of retreat for anyone trapped high. Water that has cascaded down the black limestone walls in the relative warmth of the storm freezes solid in the cold front that always follows. Previously dry rock becomes glazed with verglas, a glassy sheen of hard water ice, filling the cracks and fissures and covering all protection points. The rock itself is layered in a distinctive downward strata so that all holds are now sloping, ice-coated and lethally treacherous. 1

The concave shape of the vast wall seems to generate its own distinct weather systems so that while a ferocious storm lashes the wall the meadows below bask in sunshine. Far below, yet less than an hour's walk from the foot of the face, tourists crowd the terraces of the hotels and peer morbidly through binoculars and telescopes at the life and death struggles being enacted on the wall above them. 2

The Eiger has a well-earned reputation as a killer. At one point the north face became so notorious that the Swiss government banned all climbing on the wall, something unheard of in the history of alpine climbing – but still climbers came and men died. Since then the fearsome reputation of the mountain has grown. Despite the huge advance in climbing standards, the Eiger north face remains the pre-eminent alpine route coveted by aspiring alpinists. For those given the grace to succeed, it is an achievement for which they are forever grateful and which they will never forget. 3

The first ascent in 1938 was one of the great landmarks of modern mountaineering, comparable with the ascents of Nanga Parbat, Annapurna and later Everest in the way in which it advanced the standards. The great climbers of the 1930s, 1940s and 1950s – Kasparek and Harrer, Herman Bühl and Diemberger, Cassin and Bonatti, Lachenal and Terray – became my inspirational heroes. It was their standards, ethics and traditions that guided me in the formative years of my climbing life. Now, in my fortieth year, there was still one thing missing from my climbing career: the north face of the Eiger. For years I had shied away from its imposing shadow, persuading myself that I didn't really want to attempt the face. I knew all along that this was a thinly disguised lie. 4

Eleven years after reading Heinrich Harrer's *The White Spider* I was to find myself hanging helplessly on a single strand of rope in a storming, freezing Andean night waiting to die. It had eerie and disturbing parallels with the death of Toni Kurz on the Eiger in 1937. That experience convinced me that I would never climb the north face of the Eiger. 5

Yet, as I watched the videos that Ray* had sent me I found myself studying the terrain, judging the technical difficulty of the climb. With mounting excitement I began to realise that his idea was not quite as half-witted as I had first thought. 6

I was now vastly more experienced as a mountaineer. I was no longer the driven, ambitious and obsessed climber of my youth, and although caution and a highly attuned sense of mortality may well have held me back on some occasions it had also meant that I was still alive. The boldness and confidence of youth can lead to striking success or tragic failure. The wariness of age and experience can be just as paralysing. It can be a very fine line to tread and I felt we had the balance about right. 7

It was a neat little rationale that I found myself warming to as I watched the climbers making their way steadily up the north face. When they finally reached the summit ridge I knew with growing excitement that Ray was right. We had at least to make an attempt on the route. We would regret it for the rest of our lives if we never even went up to the bottom of the face and had, as he put it, 'a wee look'. If either of us didn't like what we saw we would just walk away. 8

* Ray — a friend, and climbing companion, of Joe Simpson